Megan Morgan 2009

GERMAN
FOR BEGINNERS
PUZZLE WORKBOOK
Shopping and Eating

Rachel Bladon

Illustrated by John Shackell

Designed by Diane Thistlethwaite

Language consultant: Sandy Walker

Additional advice from Beate Bowler and Anke Kornmüller

Series editor: Nicole Irving

CONTENTS

die Kassette

das Eis

das Buch

das Bonbon

der Comic

der Apfel

der Bleistift

die Schokolade

Shopping

In this book, all the German words you will need to do the puzzles are shown in the Word checks and the pictures. There are also some words on page 1. You can find answers to all the puzzles on pages 28 to 30.

The puzzles on these two pages will help you say hello and goodbye to people when you are shopping. They also practise some useful German words for things.

Word check

guten Morgen	good morning
guten Tag	hello, good day
guten Abend	good evening
auf Wiedersehen	goodbye
Herr	Mr.
Frau	Mrs.

When greeting an adult you don't know well, it is polite to add their name if you know it, for example **Guten Morgen, Frau Braun** (Good morning, Mrs. Braun).

danke (**schön**)	thank you (very much)
bitte schön	there you are, there you go
Entschuldigung	sorry

Words for things

Words for things (called "nouns") are all either "masculine", "feminine" or "neuter" in German. The word for "the" is **der** before masculine nouns, **die** before feminine ones and **das** before neuter ones.

All German nouns begin with a capital letter. Always try to learn them with the right word for "the".

der Pfirsich	peach
der Schal	scarf
die Briefmarke	stamp
die Aprikose	apricot
das T-shirt	T-shirt
das Poster	poster

Talking nonsense

In this shop, the things that the people are saying have been swapped around. Can you write what each person should be saying next to their name in the box at the bottom of the page?

Guten Tag, Herr Schmidt.

Herr Schmidt

Entschuldigung.

Frau Fischer

Danke schön.

die Mütze

die Apfelsine

die Birne

Stefan

Guten Tag, Frau Fischer.

Bitte schön.

Auf Wiedersehen.

Nils

Christoph

die Torte

der Blumenkohl

Petra

die Banane

der Keks

die Blume

Nils:

Stefan:

Petra:

Frau Fischer:

Christoph:

Herr Schmidt:

Word search

The German names of nine things are hidden in this grid without **der**, **die** or **das**. Can you find them and write them out with the correct words for "the"? Use one list for **der** words, one for **die** words and another for **das** words.* Remember, all the words you will need are shown on these two pages or on page 1.

A	B	L	U	M	E	E	H	M	T
U	L	R	B	G	B	O	Ü	C	P
P	E	I	H	N	J	T	S	E	A
C	I	B	R	L	Z	C	O	S	D
K	S	U	L	E	T	Z	B	O	Y
Y	T	C	E	F	T	V	J	K	I
A	I	H	H	P	A	S	E	I	S
K	F	W	S	A	M	F	O	R	U
F	T	D	Z	M	L	N	H	P	G
J	I	R	L	D	V	G	F	A	W

der

1. ....
2. ....
3. ....

die

1. ....
2. ....
3. ....

das

1. ....
2. ....
3. ....

In shape

Each part of the shape below has German words on it. Shade in all the parts that show the name of something you can eat. Then twist the page around, and you will see something you recognize. Write the German name for what you see in the grey space. (Don't forget **der**, **die** or **das**.)

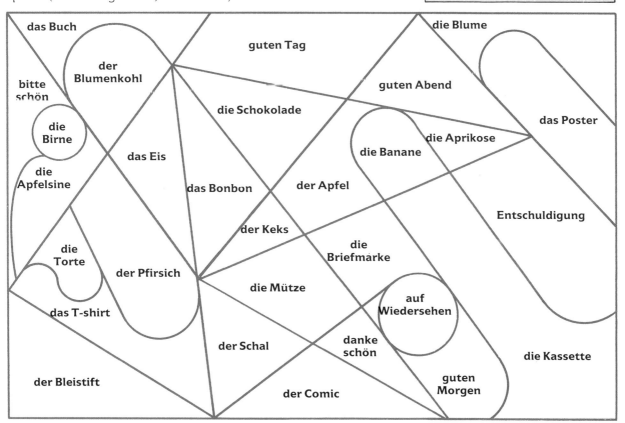

das Buch

der Blumenkohl

guten Tag

die Blume

bitte schön

guten Abend

die Schokolade

das Poster

die Birne

die Aprikose

das Eis

die Banane

die Apfelsine

das Bonbon

der Apfel

Entschuldigung

der Keks

die Torte

die Briefmarke

der Pfirsich

die Mütze

das T-shirt

auf Wiedersehen

der Schal

danke schön

die Kassette

der Bleistift

der Comic

guten Morgen

Shopping around

Here are some puzzles which use lots of the German words you need for buying things. They also give you practice of shop names.

Word check

das Geschäft	shop, store
die Drogerie	chemist's
die Apotheke*	chemist's, pharmacy
die Bäckerei	baker's
die Metzgerei	butcher's
der Gemüsehändler	greengrocer's
die Konditorei	cake shop
der Supermarkt	supermarket
das Kaufhaus**	department store
das Feinkostgeschäft	delicatessen
der Zeitungshändler	newsagent's
die Post	post office

You will also find a very small shop or stall called **der Kiosk** (kiosk). This sells drinks, sweets, postcards and newspapers.

der Ring	ring
das Stück Torte	piece/slice of cake
das Brötchen	bread roll
die Postkarte	postcard
die Zahnbürste	toothbrush

"A" or "an" is **ein** before **der** and **das** words and **eine** before **die** words:

ein Apfel	an apple
ein Brötchen	a bread roll
eine Zahnbürste	a toothbrush

ich möchte	I would like
bitte	please
ja	yes
nein	no
was kostet das?	how much is it/that?
was macht das?	how much does that come to?

German money: **eine Mark = 100 Pfennig**.

eine Mark	one mark
zwei Mark	two marks
fünfzig Pfennig	fifty pfennigs

On shop signs, you will often see **Mark** written as **DM**.

Shopping in Kaufburg

Gabi has drawn pictures of the six things she wants to buy. She gets them all in the order shown on her list, buying one thing from each shop in Kaufburg. Can you mark Gabi's route on the town plan? (She never goes along the same part of a street twice.)

Write six sentences in the blue boxes to show how Gabi asks for the things on her list. (Begin each one with **Ich möchte ein** or **Ich möchte eine** ...)

1. ....

....

2. ....

....

3. ....

Cartoon confusion

Two separate cartoon stories, each made up of six pictures, have been jumbled up (below and on the right). The first picture of one story is marked "1", and the first picture of the other story is marked "A". Decide which pictures make up which story. Then mark them in order, from 2 to 6 and B to F.

---

* The difference between **die Apotheke** and **die Drogerie** is that only **die Apotheke** sells prescribed medicines.

** A German **Kaufhaus** sells most things: clothes, stationery, toiletries and food as well.

● der Kiosk ● die Post

● der Gemüsehändler

die Bäckerei ●

die Konditorei ● der Supermarkt
●

Word chain

In this grid, the German names for the twelve things listed below are arranged in a chain (without words for "the"). To find them, start from the middle letter "Z" and move up, down, left or right by one or more letters. Then, in the blue box, write out the words you have found. (Keep to the order of the word chain and add **der, die or das**.)

bread roll   cake
cap   cassette
pear   pencil
postcard   supermarket
sweet   toothbrush
T-shirt

M	Ü	T	Z	E	T	T	E	S
T	F	I	E	B	O	N	B	S
O	R	T	S	I	E	L	O	A
T	T	E	R	N	E	B	N	K
T	R	B	I	Z	Ü	R	S	T
H	I	T	R	A	B	U	S	E
S	T	E	A	H	N	P	E	R
O	S	T	K	T	Ö	T	K	M
P	N	E	H	C	R	B	R	A

4. ....

....

5. ....

....

6. ....

....

Guten Tag.

Auf Wiedersehen, Herr Müller.

Bitte schön.

Danke schön. Was kostet das?

Fünfzig Pfennig, bitte.

Danke schön. Was kostet das?

Guten Abend, Herr Müller. Ich möchte ein Brötchen, bitte.

A

1. ....

2. ....

3. ....

4. ....

5. ....

6. ....

7. ....

8. ....

9. ....

10. ....

11. ....

At the market

These puzzles are all about counting up to twenty and buying things from the market.

Numbers 1-20

1	eins	11	elf
2	zwei	12	zwölf
3	drei	13	dreizehn
4	vier	14	vierzehn
5	fünf	15	fünfzehn
6	sechs	16	sechzehn
7	sieben	17	siebzehn
8	acht	18	achtzehn
9	neun	19	neunzehn
10	zehn	20	zwanzig

"One" is **eins** when you use it on its own. It is **ein** before masculine and neuter words and **eine** before feminine ones.*

A noun is "plural" when you are talking about more than one thing (for example, "birds"). Many German nouns change when they turn into plurals. Some add one or two letters. Others add a sign called an umlaut (¨). A few add an umlaut and letters.

"The" before a plural noun is **die**. In this book, [pl] after a noun shows that it is plural. **

die Blumen [pl]	flowers
die Äpfel [pl]	apples
die Bücher [pl]	books

Word check

Here is the German action word, or verb, **haben** (to have, to have got). Like all verbs, it changes (has slightly different words) when different people do the action:

ich habe	I have (got)
du hast	you have (got)
er/sie hat	he/she has (got)
wir haben	we have (got)
ihr habt	you have (got)
Sie haben	you have (got)
sie haben	they have (got)

Notice that German has three words for "you", **du**, **ihr** and **Sie**. You use **du** when you are talking to a friend, a relative or a young person, and **ihr** when you are talking to more than one.

For one or more adults that you don't know well, you use **Sie**. **Sie** is the polite word for "you". It is the same as the word for "she" and "they", except that it always has a capital "s".

hast du?, habt ihr?, haben Sie?	do you have?
das macht	that comes to
und	and
der Markt	market
der Käsehändler	cheese seller, cheese stall
die Tüte	bag

Market mix-up

While Katie is on holiday in Germany, she goes to the market to buy food for a picnic with her pen pal. Decide what everyone would say in these situations, and put A, B or C in each speech bubble to show which is the right piece of German.

1. At the fruit and vegetable stall, Katie says "good morning" to the woman who is serving:

A. **Guten Morgen.**
B. **Guten Abend.**
C. **Auf Wiedersehen.**

2. She asks for some fruit for the picnic:

A. **Ich möchte eine Birne und zwei Blumen, bitte.**
B. **Ich möchte ein Bonbon und eine Aprikose, bitte.**
C. **Ich möchte zwei Äpfel und eine Banane, bitte.**

3. Apples are 50 pfennigs each, and bananas are one mark. When Katie asks how much she has to pay, she is told:

A. **Das macht eine Mark.**
B. **Das macht zwei Mark.**
C. **Das macht drei Mark.**

4. When she has paid, she asks:

A. **Hast du eine Tüte, bitte?**
B. **Habt ihr eine Tüte, bitte?**
C. **Haben Sie eine Tüte, bitte?**

5. The woman hands her a bag and replies:

A. **Nein.**
B. **Ja. Bitte schön.**
C. **Ja, danke.**

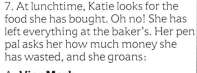

6. Katie stops at the cheese stall, where she spends six marks, and then goes to the baker's. She asks for two rolls, and the man serving says:

A. **Zwei Brötchen? Zwei Mark, bitte.**
B. **Eine Aprikose? Fünfzig Pfennig, bitte.**
C. **Ein Brötchen? Eine Mark, bitte.**

7. At lunchtime, Katie looks for the food she has bought. Oh no! She has left everything at the baker's. Her pen pal asks her how much money she has wasted, and she groans:

A. **Vier Mark.**
B. **Zehn Mark.**
C. **Neun Mark.**

* Remember, **ein** and **eine** also mean "a" (or "an").
** Plural nouns you need for puzzles are shown in the Word checks. You will find others in the Word list on pages 31-32.

Big spenders

Find what these children are saying in the box below and fill in their speech bubbles. (You will not need everything in the box.)

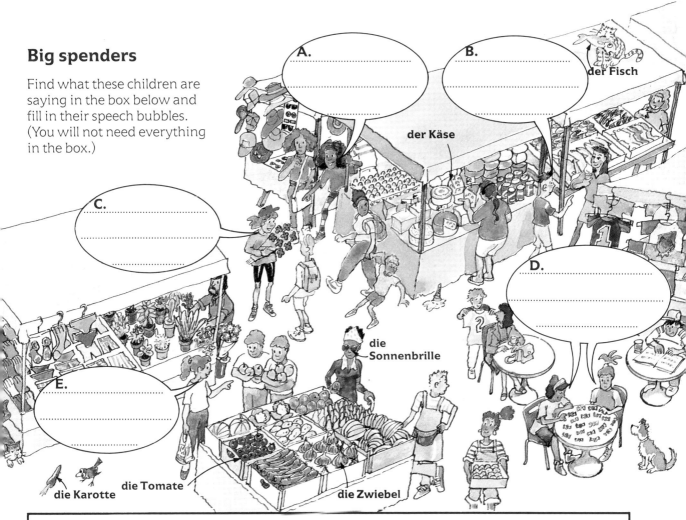

A. ....

B. ....

C. ....

D. ....

E. ....

der Fisch

der Käse

die Sonnenbrille

die Karotte

die Tomate

die Zwiebel

Ich habe neun Blumen.	Ihr habt ein Eis.	Er hat eine Mütze.
Du hast ein Eis.	Ich habe acht Blumen.	Sie hat eine Mütze.
Du hast sieben Äpfel.	Wir haben achtzehn Bonbons.	Ihr habt sieben Äpfel.

Clued-up

Use the clues below to write out the correct German numbers across the grid. Your answers will spell another number down the grey column. Look at the sums A, B, C, D and E (below right), and circle the one that gives you this number.

1. Wonders of the world.
2. Legs on a tripod.
3. Legs on a spider.
4. Unlucky for some.
5. Months in a year.
6. Players in a soccer team.
7. Half a dozen.
8. Toes on one foot.

A. **Zwanzig – drei.**
B. **Acht + neun.**
C. **Drei × fünf.**
D. **Zwei × acht.**
E. **Vier + zwei.**

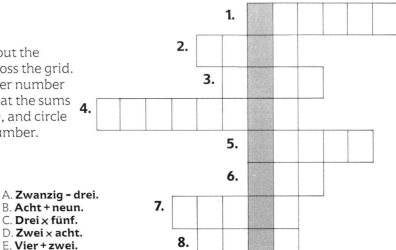

At the supermarket

These puzzles use lots of the German you need for shopping in supermarkets.

Word check

der Eingang	entrance
der Ausgang	exit
geöffnet	open
geschlossen	closed
der Einkaufswagen	trolley
der Einkaufskorb (die Einkaufskörbe [pl])	basket
die Kleider [pl]	clothes
die Sportartikel [pl]	sports gear
das Brot	bread
das Fleisch	meat
der Schinken	ham
die Chips [pl]	crisps
eine Tüte Chips	a packet of crisps
die Kekse [pl]	biscuits
das Wasser	water

In German, the way you normally say things like "I have got some sweets" (or "I have got sweets") is to use the plural noun without any word for "some" (and without **die**). For "I have got (some) sweets", you say **ich habe Bonbons**.

ein Päckchen*	a packet (of)
ein Stück*	a piece (of)
eine Scheibe*	a slice (of)
ein Kilo*	a kilo (of)
hundert Gramm*	a hundred grammes (of)
etwas mehr	a little more
etwas weniger	a little less
sonst noch etwas?	anything else?
soviel?	this much?, like that?
wo ist?	where is?
wo sind?	where are?
sind	are
da drüben	over there
am	by the, at the

When a German verb is followed by the name of a thing (as in "I would like the pencil"), you use different words for "the" and "a" (or "an") if the thing is masculine. You use **den** instead of **der**, and **einen** instead of **ein**, for example:

ich möchte den Bleistift	I would like the pencil
ich habe einen Apfel	I have got an apple

* After these pieces of German, you drop **der**, **die** and **das**.

Torn in two

Pair off the pieces of German in these blue labels to find six sentences. Then look at the pictures below. Can you match each of the sentences with a speech bubble to make six little conversations? Fill in the spaces 1 to 6 with the right sentences.

die Einkaufskörbe, bitte?

sind die Kekse, bitte?

mehr, bitte.   sechs Mark.

Ja, bitte. Und ein Stück

Käse.

Wo   Etwas

Ein Kilo

Äpfel, bitte.

Wo sind   Das macht

1.

2.

3.

4.

5.

6.

Was macht das?

Soviel?

Sonst noch etwas?

Eine Scheibe Schinken?

Da drüben, am Eingang.

Die Kekse sind da drüben.

Twin shoppers

Kirstin and Stefan have each bought three things that the other did not get. Can you write three sentences to say which things only Kirstin has, and three to say which ones only Stefan has? Begin your answers with the German for "She has ..." or "He has ...", and use the correct German for "a" or "some".

Kirstin's things

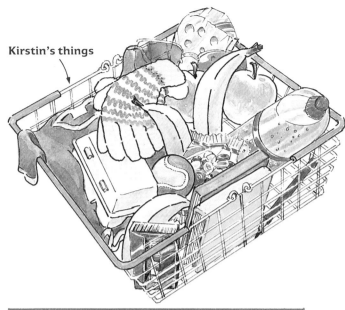

Stefan's things

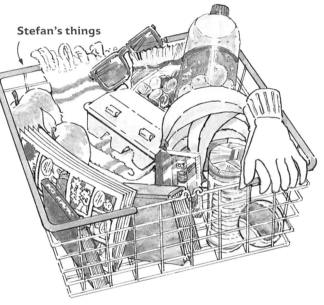

1.	
2.	
3.	
4.	
5.	
6.	

Shopping search

Hidden in this grid are the German names for the nine things that Stefanie wants to buy. Can you find them and write sentences for her to say what she wants? Begin your answers with **Ich möchte** and use the right words for "a".

P	C	Ü	E	R	W	T	J	L
O	F	C	A	S	I	L	K	P
S	B	I	F	K	D	A	M	O
T	S	M	R	N	S	C	I	S
K	E	O	T	S	H	I	R	T
A	B	C	E	O	I	H	D	E
R	G	T	T	B	U	C	H	R
T	T	A	P	F	E	L	H	Ö
E	N	I	S	L	E	F	P	A

1.	
2.	
3.	
4.	
5.	
6.	
7.	
8.	
9.	

Other shops in town

The puzzles on these two pages use shop names and lots of numbers.

Word check

die Buchhandlung	bookshop
das Fotogeschäft	camera shop
die Schreib-warenhandlung	stationer's
der Plattenladen	music shop
das Sportgeschäft	sports shop
das Bekleidungs-geschäft	clothes shop
die Bibliothek	library
das Reisebüro	travel agent's
das Verkehrsamt	tourist office

der Ball	ball
der Film	film
das Etui	pencil case
das Heft	exercise book
das Lineal	ruler
der Aufkleber	sticker
die Pflaster [pl]	plasters
die Bonbons [pl]	sweets
die Birnen [pl]	pears
die Bananen [pl]	bananas
die Apfelsinen [pl]	oranges
die Straße*	street
am Ende der Straße	at the end of the street
der Baum	tree
ist	is

hinter	behind
vor	in front of
zwischen	between
gegenüber von	opposite
neben	next to
in der Nähe von	near

When saying where things are, you use special words for "the" after the six pieces of German above. "The" turns into **dem** with masculine and neuter nouns, **der** with feminine ones and **den** with plurals. For example, "behind the library" is **hinter der Bibliothek**.

When you are talking about prices that are a mixture of marks and pfennigs, you don't use the word **Pfennig**. For example, **eine Mark fünfzig** is what you say for "one mark fifty (pfennigs)".

drei Mark (**das Stück**)	three marks (each)

Numbers 21-100

21	einundzwanzig	28	achtundzwanzig	41	einundvierzig
22	zweiundzwanzig	29	neunundzwanzig	50	fünfzig
23	dreiundzwanzig	30	dreißig	60	sechzig
24	vierundzwanzig	31	einunddreißig	70	siebzig
25	fünfundzwanzig	32	zweiunddreißig	80	achtzig
26	sechsundzwanzig	33	dreiunddreißig	90	neunzig
27	siebenundzwanzig	40	vierzig	100	hundert

Bargain hunter

Nils wants to get all the things shown on the right from one department store, but he can't decide whether it will be cheaper to go to **Preisbrecher** or **Billig**.

Look at the pricelists and decide where he should go. Then add up what he will spend if he goes there, and what he will save. Write down (in German) the name of the department store and both these amounts.

Preisbrecher

ein Heft	vier Mark zwanzig
ein Lineal	drei Mark zwanzig
ein Bleistift	achtzig Pfennig
ein Film	sechzehn Mark zehn
eine Postkarte	sechzig Pfennig
eine Zahnbürste	sechs Mark fünfzig
ein Kilo Birnen	vier Mark (fünfundsiebzig Pfennig das Stück)
ein Kilo Pfirsiche	fünf Mark (achtzig Pfennig das Stück)
hundert Gramm Bonbons	eine Mark fünfzig
eine Tüte Chips	zwei Mark

Billig

ein Kilo Birnen	drei Mark (fünfzig Pfennig das Stück)
eine Tüte Chips	zwei Mark zwanzig
eine Postkarte	dreißig Pfennig
ein Comic	zwei Mark dreißig
ein Film	vierzehn Mark sechzig
eine Kassette	neunzehn Mark sechzig
eine Zahnbürste	sieben Mark
ein Heft	zwei Mark vierzig
ein Etui	fünf Mark zehn
ein Bleistift	eine Mark
ein Lineal	drei Mark achtzig

The department store Nils should go to is: ....

He will spend: ....

He will save: ....

* The German letter ß is said like the "ss" in "Miss".

Treasure trail

This list shows seven of the eight things you have to collect here, and the order you must collect them in. Find the animal that has the first thing, and it will tell you where to go next. Now decide how the rest of the animals should direct you to the other pieces of "treasure". Fill in their speech bubbles, beginning **neben**, **vor** or **gegenüber von**. The last animal you come to will tell you where the eighth thing is. Write the German for this at the bottom of the list.

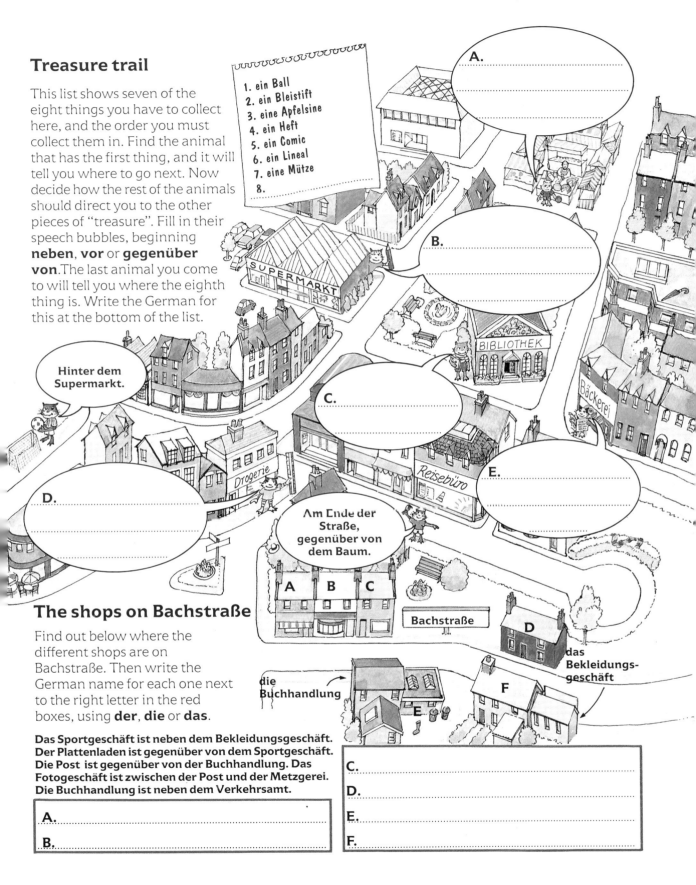

1. ein Ball
2. ein Bleistift
3. eine Apfelsine
4. ein Heft
5. ein Comic
6. ein Lineal
7. eine Mütze
8.

A.

B.

C.

D.

E.

Hinter dem Supermarkt.

Am Ende der Straße, gegenüber von dem Baum.

SUPERMARKT

BIBLIOTHEK

Drogerie

Reisebüro

Bäckerei

The shops on Bachstraße

Find out below where the different shops are on Bachstraße. Then write the German name for each one next to the right letter in the red boxes, using **der**, **die** or **das**.

die Buchhandlung

das Bekleidungs- geschäft

Bachstraße

Das Sportgeschäft ist neben dem Bekleidungsgeschäft. Der Plattenladen ist gegenüber von dem Sportgeschäft. Die Post ist gegenüber von der Buchhandlung. Das Fotogeschäft ist zwischen der Post und der Metzgerei. Die Buchhandlung ist neben dem Verkehrsamt.

A.

B.

C.

D.

E.

F.

11

Getting around town

The puzzles on these two pages help you find the bank, buy stamps and use other services. They also give you some more number practice.

Word check

der Brief	letter
die Bank	bank
der Devisenschalter	foreign exchange desk
das Geld	money
die Reiseschecks [pl]	traveller's cheques
ich möchte meine Reiseschecks einlösen	I would like to cash my traveller's cheques
der Paß	passport
die Tankstelle	petrol station
das Benzin	petrol
volltanken?	shall I fill her up (with petrol)?
volltanken, bitte	fill her up, please
das Öl kontrollieren	to check the oil
der Waschsalon	launderette
das Waschpulver	washing powder
die Telefonzelle	phone booth
entschuldigen Sie	excuse me
gibt es hier in der Nähe ein/eine ...?	is there a ... near here?
auf der linken Seite	on the left
auf der rechten Seite	on the right
könnten Sie (das Öl kontrollieren)?	could you (check the oil)?
auch	also, as well
Deutschland	Germany
für	for
oder	or
der Becher	plastic cup, beaker
nur	only

Going dotty

Join all the red dots from twenty to thirty, forty to fifty, sixty to seventy and eighty to ninety to make a maze. Then mark the route Ute must take through it to find her dog.

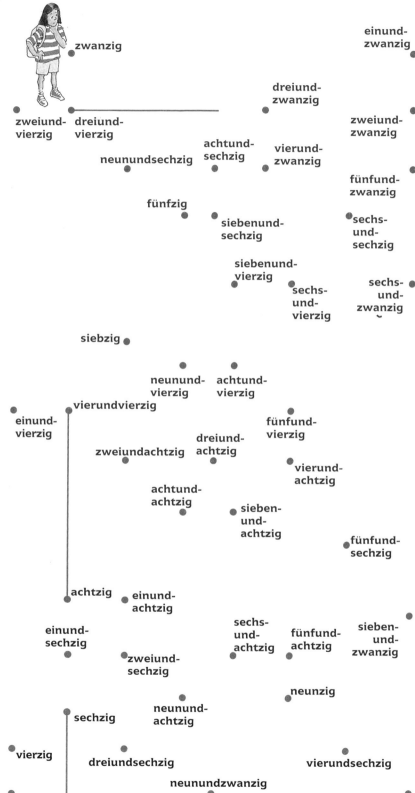

zwanzig

einundzwanzig

dreiundzwanzig

zweiundvierzig

dreiundvierzig

zweiundzwanzig

achtundsechzig

vierundzwanzig

neunundsechzig

fünfundzwanzig

fünfzig

siebenundsechzig

sechsundsechzig

siebenundvierzig

sechsundvierzig

sechsundzwanzig

siebzig

neunundvierzig

achtundvierzig

vierundvierzig

fünfundvierzig

einundvierzig

zweiundachtzig

dreiundachtzig

vierundachtzig

achtundachtzig

siebenundachtzig

fünfundsechzig

achtzig

einundachtzig

sechsundachtzig

fünfundachtzig

siebenundzwanzig

einundsechzig

zweiundsechzig

neunzig

sechzig

neunundachtzig

vierzig

dreiundsechzig

vierundsechzig

neunundzwanzig

dreißig

achtundzwanzig

12

Picture matchmaking

Can you pair off the five pieces of German, A to E, with the numbered pieces, 1 to 5, to make five conversations? Match each of these with the correct picture and write the letter and number in the small boxes provided.

A. **Gibt es hier in der Nähe eine Post?**
B. **Haben Sie Waschpulver?**
C. **Volltanken?**
D. **Eine Briefmarke für eine Postkarte, bitte.**
E. **Ich möchte meine Reiseschecks einlösen, bitte.**

1. **Ja. Und könnten Sie auch das Öl kontrollieren, bitte?**
2. **Für Deutschland?**
3. **Paß, bitte.**
4. **Ja, auf der linken Seite, gegenüber von der Apotheke.**
5. **Ja, zwei Mark der Becher.**

Postcard palaver

First read this story about Louise and Martin trying to send a postcard home to Manchester. Then fill in the gaps in the numbered pieces of German (shown in heavier lettering). Write each piece out in the red box, adding the missing words.

Louise and Martin wanted a stamp for their postcard, so they stopped someone and asked: **1) "Entschuldigen Sie. Wo ist ...?"** When they got to the post office, Louise explained what she wanted: **2) "Ich möchte ..., bitte."** Seeing the postcard in Louise's hand, the woman at the counter inquired **3) "Für eine ...?"**. **4) "..., bitte,"** Louise nodded. **5) " ..., bitte",** said the woman, and Martin rummaged in his pocket for eighty pfennigs. He frowned, took out a fifty pfennig coin and said: **6) "Ich habe nur ..."**. Louise and Martin apologized and asked: **7) "Gibt es hier in der Nähe ...?"** **8) "Ja. Auf ..., neben ... ."** the woman replied. They thanked her, said goodbye: **9)**

"Danke schön. ...", and set off for the bank.

Sure enough, Louise and Martin found the bank on the right, next to the bookshop. They asked a cashier where the foreign exchange counter was: **10) "Wo ist ...?"** Louise explained what she wanted: **11) "Ich möchte ..., bitte."** But the man at the desk shook his head - they did not cash traveller's cheques at that branch. He told Louise and Martin to take a bus to the bank at Farburg.

An hour later, their pockets full of German marks, Louise and Martin returned to the post office. "Oh no!" cried Martin, pointing at the sign on the door, which read **12) "..."**. "It's closed!"

1.

2.

3.

4.

5.

6.

7.

8.

9.

10.

11.

12.

Opening hours

Here you can practise talking about the opening and closing times of shops and other useful places.

Telling the time

wie spät ist es?	what time is it?
es ist	it is
(es ist) ein Uhr	(it is) one o'clock
acht Uhr	eight o'clock
Mittag	midday, twelve o'clock
nach	past
fünf nach acht	five past eight
zwanzig nach drei	twenty past three
vor	to
zehn vor eins*	ten to one
fünfundzwanzig vor vier	twenty-five to four
Viertel nach (vier)	quarter past (four)
Viertel vor (elf)	quarter to (eleven)
halb	half

In German, instead of saying "half past", you say "half to" the next hour, for example:

es ist halb neun	it is half past eight
es ist halb drei	it is half past two

Word check

morgens	in the morning
abends	in the evening
um (sechs Uhr)	at (six o'clock)
von ... bis	from ... until

When you are talking about shop opening hours, the words **geöffnet** (open) and **geschlossen** (closed) always go to the end of the sentence:

die Bank ist von acht Uhr morgens bis sechs Uhr abends geöffnet	the bank is open from eight o'clock in the morning until six o'clock in the evening

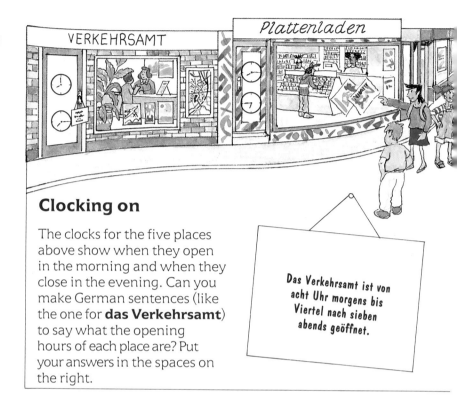

Clocking on

The clocks for the five places above show when they open in the morning and when they close in the evening. Can you make German sentences (like the one for **das Verkehrsamt**) to say what the opening hours of each place are? Put your answers in the spaces on the right.

Das Verkehrsamt ist von acht Uhr morgens bis Viertel nach sieben abends geöffnet.

Word circle

Look at the things numbered 1 to 5. For each one, think of a place where you might buy it. Then write the German name for this place around the word circle, without using words for "the". Its first letter must go in the space with the matching number, then one letter goes into each space until you reach the next number. (Three spaces already have letters in them.)

Now you will see something spelled out in the section shown by the arrow. Use the five letters in grey spaces to spell the name for a place where you might buy this. Write this name in the space below, adding the word for "the".

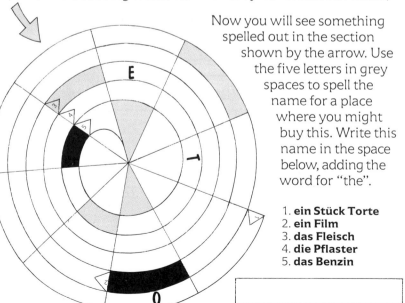

1. **ein Stück Torte**
2. **ein Film**
3. **das Fleisch**
4. **die Pflaster**
5. **das Benzin**

* Notice that, when telling the time, "one o'clock" is **ein Uhr**, but "one" is **eins**.

1. ....
....
2. ....
....
3. ....
....
4. ....
....

Out of time

First read about the problems Lothar's friends are having with their watches (see right). Then fill in the speech bubbles to show how they all answer the waiter's question.

Stefan's watch is always ten minutes fast and Gabi's always runs a quarter of an hour slower than his. Ute's watch is usually fifteen minutes slow, but it stopped half an hour ago. Stefanie reset her watch by Ute's an hour ago, and since then it has kept good time. Only Lothar's is showing the right time.

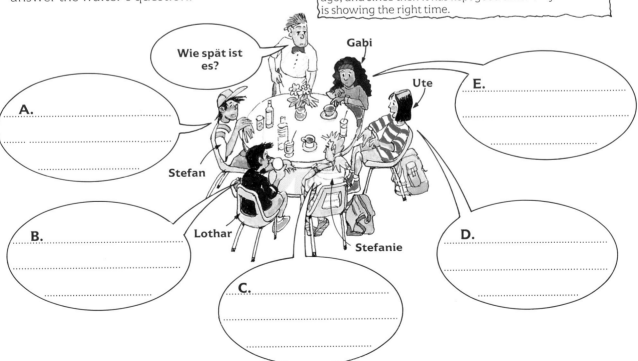

Jamjam Island

The puzzles on Jamjam Island will help you talk about things you like eating.

Word check

Here is the verb **essen** (to eat):

ich esse	I eat
du ißt	you eat
er/sie/es ißt	he/she/it eats
wir essen	we eat
ihr eßt	you eat
Sie essen	you eat
sie essen	they eat

For "it" in German, you use **er** to talk about a masculine word, **sie** for a feminine word and **es** for a neuter one.

When talking about food, to say that you like something, you use **essen** with **gern** added on. For example, **ich esse gern Kekse** means "I like (eating) biscuits".

das Frühstück	breakfast
das Mittagessen	lunch
das Abendessen	dinner (evening meal)
das Picknick	picnic
ich habe Hunger	I'm hungry
ich habe Durst	I'm thirsty
der Berliner (**die Berliner** [pl])	doughnut
die Pastete	pâté
das Würstchen (**die Würstchen** [pl])	sausage
das Gemüse	vegetables
die Kartoffel	potato
die Erbsen [pl]	peas
die Tomaten [pl]	tomatoes
die Zwiebeln [pl]	onions
das Obst	fruit
die Erdbeere (**die Erdbeeren** [pl])	strawberry
die Getränke [pl]	drinks
der Orangensaft	orange juice
der Kaffee	coffee
der Tee	tea

Which way?

Unscramble the words below to find the German names of eight things. Find these things on the island, then, for each one, write its name out on the blank sign that points along the road leading to it.

KICKSPINCAD

SHIDEEDACLOOK

RICHNÜDESTEW

DREIBLINERE

MATTIENODE

HICISPED

BLINDWEEZIE

RODFASTGRANNEE

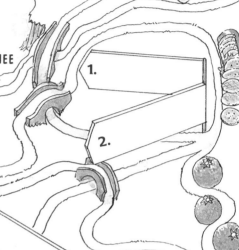

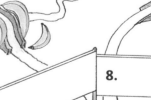

Triple treat

Below, Petra and her friends are all saying what things they like eating. Can you spot these things on the island, and then find the route each of them must take to get there? Along these routes, they will each find two other things they like. Write sentences below for all the characters shown, saying what these two things are. (Begin with the German for "He likes", "She likes", "It likes" or "They like".)

Wir essen gern Berliner.

Ich esse gern Schokolade.

Ich esse gern Birnen.

Ich esse gern Würstchen.

Wir essen gern Chips.

1. ....
2. ....
3. ....
4. ....
5. ....

Gemüse
1. ....
2. ....
3. ....
4. ....

Getränke
1. ....
2. ....
3. ....
4. ....

Fleisch
1. ....
2. ....
3. ....

Obst
1. ....
2. ....
3. ....
4. ....
5. ....
6. ....

6. ....

Food sails

Look at the labels on these four ships' flags. Then decide which of the things listed below go with which flag, and write them in the spaces on the correct sail. (There are five things on the list that you will not use.)

der Tee	das Wasser
der Apfel	die Birne
das Würstchen	die Erbsen
das Bonbon	der Schinken
der Pfirsich	die Apfelsine
die Kartoffel	die Schokolade
das Eis	der Kaffee
die Aprikose	die Karotte
der Orangensaft	die Banane
die Torte	die Pastete
das Brötchen	die Zwiebel

17

Likes and dislikes

Here you can get more practice of saying what food you like. These puzzles will also help you talk about the things you don't like eating.

Word check

Below you can see the verb **trinken** (to drink). Most German verbs change in the same way as **trinken** when different people do the action:

ich trinke	I drink
du trinkst	you drink
er/sie/es trinkt	he/she/it drinks
wir trinken	we drink
ihr trinkt	you drink
Sie trinken	you drink
sie trinken	they drink

To say what food you like, you use **essen** with **gern**.* For all types of drinks, you use **trinken** with **gern**:

ich trinke gern Orangensaft	I like (drinking) orange juice

To say what you prefer, you add **lieber** (instead of **gern**):

ich trinke lieber Kaffee	I prefer (drinking) coffee
ich esse lieber Fleisch	I prefer (eating) meat

die Nudeln [pl]	pasta
die Spaghetti [pl]	spaghetti
das Omelett	omelette
der Hamburger	hamburger
die Pommes frites [pl]	chips
die Pizza	pizza
die Brote [pl]	sandwiches
das Schinkenbrot	ham sandwich
das Käsebrot	cheese sandwich
der Salat	salad
die Suppe	soup
die Milch	milk
die Eier [pl]	eggs
aber	but
ich bin Vegetarier	I am a vegetarian (if you are a boy or man)
ich bin Vegetarierin	I am a vegetarian (girl or woman)
das Café	café

In German, to say things like "I do not eat" and "I do not like", you put **nicht** (not) straight after the verb:

ich esse nicht	I do not/don't eat
ich esse nicht gern	I do not/don't like (eating)

*See page 16.

Sentence splitters

Four sentences have been cut into four pieces and mixed up. The first piece of each one is written out in the box below. Can you fit the other pieces back together and write them in the correct spaces to complete each sentence?

> nicht gern Pommes frites.

> aber er

> nicht gern Orangensaft.

> ißt nicht gern Suppe.

> ißt

> essen gern

> gern Pizza, aber du

> trinke gern

> trinkt lieber Tee.

> Spaghetti, aber wir essen

> trinkt gern Kaffee,

> Milch, aber ich trinke

1. Wir
....
....
2. Ich
....
3. Du
....
4. Er
....
....

The perfect picnic

Read what Stefanie and her friends are saying about what they especially like or dislike. Then look at the three picnic tables, A, B and C. Can you decide who should sit where, so that no one has anything they don't want on their table, and everyone has the thing they most like? Write two names on each table's list to show where everyone should sit.

On this picnic, there are two things that more than one person likes, and two things that more than one person doesn't like. Complete the four sentences in the orange sheet on the right to say what each pair of friends likes or dislikes.

> Ich esse gern Chips. Ich esse nicht gern Tomaten, und ich trinke nicht gern Kaffee.

> Ich esse gern Brote, aber ich esse lieber Kekse. Ich bin Vegetarier.

Lothar

Stefanie

A.

German crossword

Use the clues to fill in the crossword. (Don't forget the different words for "a" or "the".)

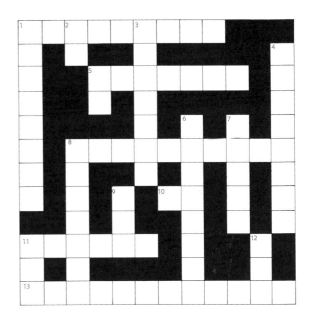

Across

1. Italians eat a lot of this. (3, 6)
5. Apples, pears and bananas are all examples of this. (3, 4)
8. Sausages, chicken and ham are all examples of this. (3, 7)
10. "It" for a **das** word. (2)
11. You can drink this on its own, or with milk or lemon. (3, 3)
13. The German for "he likes milk" is "... **Milch**". (2, 6, 4)

Down

1. It might have lots of bones. (3, 5)
2. The German for "he". (2)
3. For a drink or a snack, you go to ... (3, 4)
4. They are crunchy and come in different flavours. (3, 5)
5. "You" (when talking to someone you know well). (2)
6. It is often made with tomatoes, lettuce and cucumber. (3, 5)
7. The German for "to eat". (5)
8. It can be brown or white. (3, 4)
9. The German for "she". (3)
11. "The" in front of a feminine noun. (3)
12. "The" in front of a masculine noun. (3)

Mealtime talk

Here are some puzzles which use lots of the German you need when you get a meal ready or eat with other people.

Word check

die Küche	kitchen
der Backofen	oven
die Spüle	sink
der Kühlschrank	fridge
der Stuhl	chair
die Bratpfanne	frying pan
der Kochtopf	saucepan
der Teller (die Teller [pl])	plate
das Glas (die Gläser [pl])	glass
die Gabel (die Gabeln [pl])	fork
der Löffel (die Löffel [pl])	spoon

das Mehl	flour
der Zucker	sugar
das Salz	salt
die Konfitüre	jam
das Essen ist fertig	come to the table, it's ready
schmeckt's?	is it good?
es schmeckt sehr gut	it's delicious
noch ...?	some more ...?
ich bin satt	I've had enough (to eat)
sind	are
in	in
unter	under
auf	on

When saying where things are, you use special words for "the" after **in**, **unter** or **auf**. You use **dem** with masculine and neuter nouns, **der** with feminine ones and **den** with plurals.*

kann ich dir helfen?	can I help you? (talking to one person)
kann ich euch helfen?	can I help you? (talking to more than one person)
greif zu	help yourself
greift zu	help yourselves
reich mir bitte (die Erbsen)	can you pass me (the peas), please?

You only use the five pieces of German above when talking to friends, relatives or people your own age. For adults you don't know well, you say:

kann ich Ihnen helfen?	can I help you?
greifen Sie zu	help yourself, help yourselves
reichen Sie mir bitte (die Erbsen)	can you pass me (the peas), please?

Hungry campers

Find what these children are saying in the panel on the side of the tent, and fill in each of their speech bubbles. (You will not need everything in the panel.)

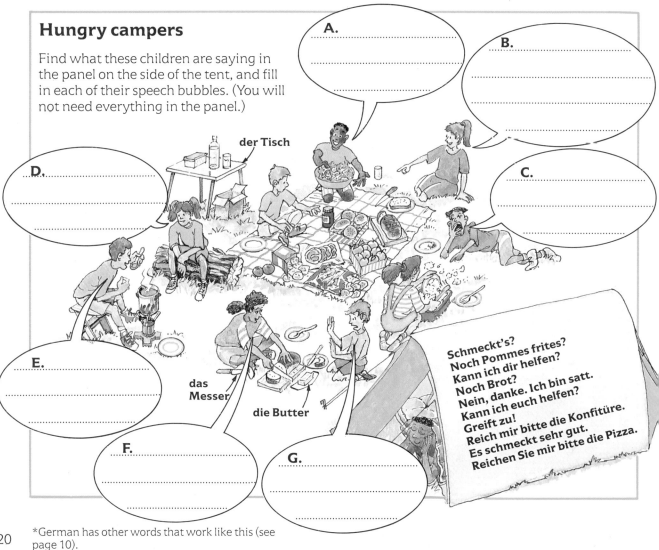

A.

B.

C.

D.

E.

F.

G.

der Tisch

das Messer

die Butter

Schmeckt's?
Noch Pommes frites?
Kann ich dir helfen?
Noch Brot?
Nein, danke. Ich bin satt.
Kann ich euch helfen?
Greift zu!
Reich mir bitte die Konfitüre.
Es schmeckt sehr gut.
Reichen Sie mir bitte die Pizza.

*German has other words that work like this (see page 10).

Kitchen caper

Picture A below shows what the Schnitzel family kitchen looked like before Andrea started cooking. Picture B shows what it looks like afterwards. Decide which things Andrea has put away in the wrong place, then write German sentences to say where these things are now, using the words for "in", "on" or "under".

1. ....
   ....

2. ....

3. ....

4. ....

5. ....

6. ....

7. ....

8. ....

Word snake

Think of the German names for the things listed in the grey box. Write them along the word snake, putting the first letter of each one next to its number. Now fill the red grid with the circled letters, arranging them so they spell the name of something you can make with these things.

1. CHEESE
2. SALT
3. BUTTER
4. EGGS
5. MILK
6. A FRYING PAN

		O				

In the café

The puzzles on these two pages give you lots of practice of asking for things in cafés.

Word check

der Kaffee	coffee
der Tee	tea
mit Milch	with milk
mit Zitrone	with lemon
die heiße Schokolade	hot chocolate
ein Glas	a glass (of)
die Cola	coke
der Apfelsaft	apple juice
bitte sehr?	what would you like?

ich nehme (eine Cola) — I'll have (a coke)

When asking for something, you often drop the verb and say things like "A tea, please", meaning "I'll have a tea, please". If what you are asking for is masculine, you must use special words for "the" and "a",* even though you have dropped the verb:

ich nehme einen Tee, bitte — I'll have a tea, please
einen Tee, bitte — a tea, please

es tut mir leid	I'm sorry
die Menschen [pl]	people
die Frau	woman
der Kellner	waiter

der Detektiv	detective
bringen	to bring
fragen	to ask
er/sie liest	he/she is reading
es gibt	there is/are
ich bin	I am
also	well, so

noch ein/noch eine	another
kein/keine	no, none
es ist kein/keine ... mehr da	there is no more ...

You use **noch ein, kein** and **es ist kein ... mehr da** in front of masculine or neuter nouns. With feminine nouns you use **noch eine, keine** and **es ist keine ... mehr da**.

Crime cracker

The detective in this picture is reporting on the movements of the criminal Lieselotte Mess, but he is very tired and is making lots of mistakes. Can you write what he should be saying in the space below, changing the things that are wrong?

> Es ist Viertel nach drei. Ich bin in dem Supermarkt gegenüber von dem Café. Es gibt vierzehn Menschen in dem Café. Lieselotte Mess ist neben Uli Gann und ißt einen Hamburger. Sie ißt Nudeln und er ißt einen Hamburger. Eine Sonnenbrille und zwei Löffel sind auch auf dem Tisch. Der Kellner bringt einen Kaffee und eine Cola.

Uli Gann
Lieselotte Mess
die Toiletten
die Quiche
die Speisekarte
die Rechnung
der Detektiv
der Pfannkuchen

....

....

....

....

....

....

....

*You have to use **den** and **einen**, as explained on page 8.

Taking orders

Below you can see what everyone wants to eat and drink. Can you write out each person's order in the red box, using the German for "I'll have a … and a …"?

1. ....
....
....
....
....
2. ....
....
....
....
....
3. ....
....
....
....
4. ....
....
....
....
5. ....
....
....
6. ....
....
....

Lunch at the Café Paradies

Can you unjumble this story to find out about Silke's visit to the Café Paradies? Put the numbers of each part of the story in the right order in the green box.

1. **"Es ist auch keine Suppe mehr da. Wir haben nur Pizza oder Schinkenbrot."**

2. **"Ja. Es gibt ein Café gegenüber von der Post. Aber es ist geschlossen."**

3. **"Ich nehme ein Stück Quiche und einen Apfelsaft, bitte."**

4. **"Also, ich nehme die Suppe."**

5. **Silke ist in dem Café Paradies. Sie liest die Speisekarte.**

6. **"Es tut mir leid. Es ist keine Quiche mehr da."**

7. **"Aber ich esse nicht gern Pizza, und ich bin Vegetarierin. Gibt es hier in der Nähe noch ein Café?" fragt Silke.**

8. **"Bitte sehr?" fragt der Kellner.**

Eating out

Here you will find puzzles which help you practise the German you need when you go out to eat.

Word check

die Speisekarte, menu
  das Tagesmenü

Most German restaurants have two kinds of menu, **die Speisekarte** and **das Tagesmenü**. **Die Speisekarte** is the normal menu. **Das Tagesmenü** has set meals which are usually cheaper.

Also good value is **das Tagesgericht**. This is the dish of the day, or "today's special".

das Restaurant	restaurant
die Vorspeise	starter
das Hauptgericht	main course
der Nachtisch	dessert, pudding
und als Nachtisch?	and (what would you like) for dessert?

In Germany, at mealtimes, it is friendly and polite to say **guten Appetit** to people when they are about to start eating. This means "enjoy your meal."

das Steak	steak
das Hähnchen	chicken
mit (Salat)	with (salad)
die Champignons [pl]	mushrooms
der Lauch	leek, leeks
der Spinat	spinach
die Karotten [pl]	carrots
der Apfelstrudel*	apple strudel
die Schokoladen-creme	chocolate mousse
der Obstsalat	fruit salad
die Sahne	cream
was für ein Eis?	what flavour ice-cream?
das Vanilleeis	vanilla ice-cream
das Erdbeereis	strawberry ice-cream
das Schokoladeneis	chocolate ice-cream
das Mokkaeis	coffee ice-cream

Out of order

The waiter in this restaurant has taken five orders without putting the table numbers on them. Decide which one came from which table. Then put the correct number on each order.

1 X Hamburger
1 X Hähnchen
1 X Salat
Pommes frites
2 X Cola

1 X Steak
Pommes frites
1 X Pizza
1 X Salat
1 X Schokoladencreme
1 X Erdbeereis

2 X Hamburger
1 X Hähnchen
1 X Salat
Pommes frites
1 X Erdbeereis
1 X Apfelstrudel
1 X Schokoladencreme

1 X Hähnchen
1 X Hamburger
1 X Salat
Pommes frites
1 X Cola
1 X Orangensaft

1 X Omelett
1 X Salat
1 X Hähnchen
Pommes frites
1 X Schokoladencreme
1 X Vanilleeis

24 *This is a favourite German dessert, made with apples, raisins and very thin pastry.

Supper splash-out

Put the six things on the right into German, and then write them out in the correct spaces (A to F) below, to complete the cartoon story.

A vanilla ice-cream, please.

Can you pass me the water, please?

One fruit salad, please. And one ice-cream.

I've got no money!

The bill, please.

One pizza with salad and one hamburger with some chips, please.

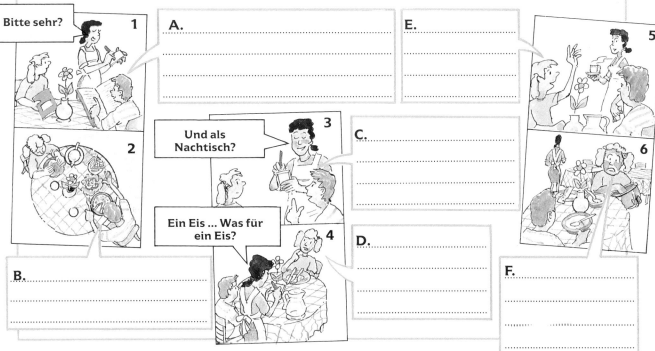

Word search

Can you find German words hidden in this grid and match them with the clues below? Write each one out next to the number of the matching clue, adding its word for "the".

1. The first meal of the day.
2. The first course.
3. The last course.
4. The place where you eat out.
5. Something you drink out of.
6. It tells you what you must pay.
7. He brings you your meal.
8. It might be the main course.
9. A kind of vegetable.
10. Something to drink.
11. You might add this to a dessert.
12. You might drink it after a meal.
13. You might use this for eating desserts.
14. You might add this to your food.

F	R	E	N	L	L	E	K	R	T
Ü	R	E	A	K	A	E	T	S	N
F	L	Ü	C	G	G	U	H	S	A
A	E	J	H	H	L	P	C	A	R
K	F	M	T	S	N	A	W	H	U
A	F	N	I	D	T	U	S	N	A
F	Ö	I	S	K	Z	Ü	N	E	T
F	L	C	C	A	L	O	C	G	S
E	E	L	H	E	A	R	A	K	E
E	S	I	E	P	S	R	O	V	R

1. ....
2. ....
3. ....
4. ....
5. ....
6. ....
7. ....
8. ....
9. ....
10. ....
11. ....
12. ....
13. ....
14. ....

Round-up

These two pages practise lots of the German that you have already used in this book.

German crossword

Use the clues to fill in the crossword. (Don't forget the different words for "a" or "the".)

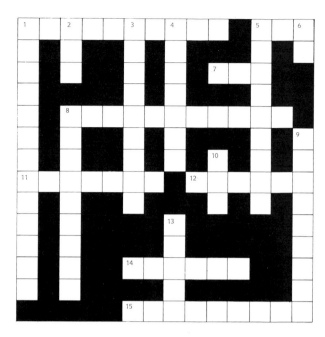

Across

1. You wear these. (3, 7)
5. "The" before a feminine noun. (3)
7. "The" before a masculine noun. (3)
8. You can buy food, clothes and lots of other things here. (3, 8)
11. You need this for baking. (3, 4)
12. It might be vanilla, strawberry or chocolate flavour. (3, 3)
14. Twelve noon. (6)
15. You spread this on bread. (3, 6)

Down

1. The evening meal. (3, 10)
2. "A" before a masculine or neuter noun. (3)
3. Most houses have a bedroom, a sitting room and .... (4, 5)
4. You can read this. (3, 4)
5. It makes things sweeter. (3, 6)
6. The German for "he". (2)
8. A kind of vegetable. (3, 6)
9. You use this for cutting things. (3, 6)
10. "The" before a neuter noun. (3)
13. The German for "please". (5)

Cracking codes

Can you crack the coded message below to find out where a stolen ring has been hidden? Write the message out properly, and then mark the place where the ring can be found in this picture.

er Dupermarkt Sst iegenüber gon vem daschsalon. Ws Eibt gine erau Fn iem dupermarkt. Sie Sat hinen einkaufswagen. Eie Sst in ier dähe Non vem dbst. Os Eibt gisch, Fpfelsaft And uarotten Kn iem dinkaufswagen. Eie Drau Fat hine eüte. Ter Ding Rst in ier düte T.

....

....

....

....

....

....

....

....

Poison maze

Stefan has to get through this maze, but the animals will only let him pass if he eats the food they are holding, and some of it is poisonous. If, at each picture junction, he follows the arrow showing what he should say in that picture, Stefan will avoid any bad food and go the right way. Find his route, then list the safe food he will eat in the red box at the bottom of the page. (Use **der**, **die** or **das**.)

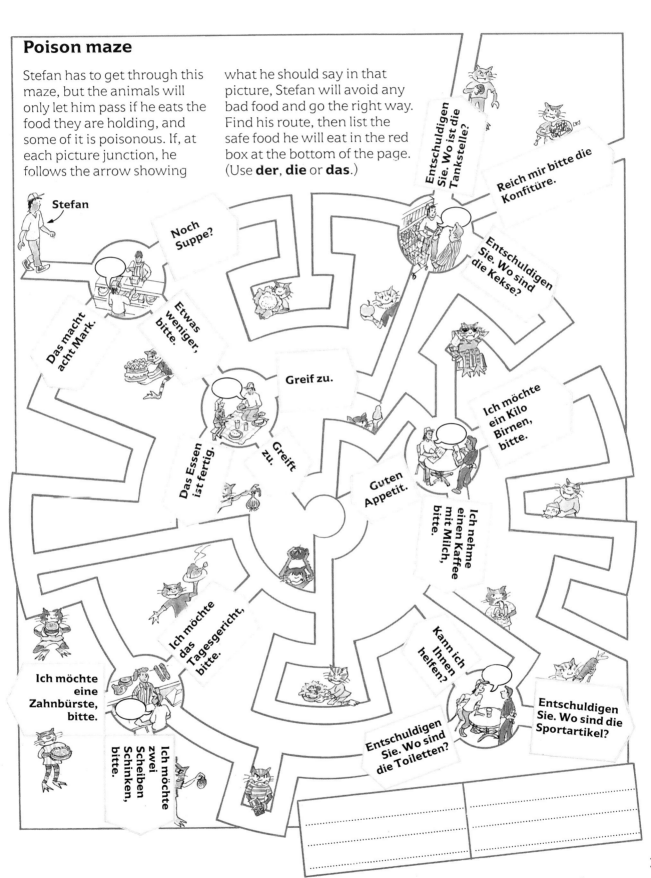

Answers to puzzles

p.2-3

Talking nonsense

Nils: Entschuldigung.
Stefan: Auf Wiedersehen.
Petra: Danke schön.
Frau Fischer: Guten Tag, Herr Schmidt.
Christoph: Bitte schön.
Herr Schmidt: Guten Tag, Frau Fischer.

Word search

The **der** words you can find are:

der Apfel
der Schal
der Bleistift

The **die** words you can find are:

die Blume
die Aprikose
die Mütze

The **das** words you can find are:

das Poster
das Buch
das Eis

In shape

The thing you can see is:

das Eis

p.4-5

Shopping in Kaufburg

Here you can see Gabi's route:

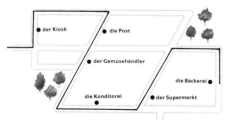

1. Ich möchte ein Bonbon, bitte.*
2. Ich möchte eine Briefmarke, bitte.
3. Ich möchte eine Banane, bitte.
4. Ich möchte ein Stück Torte, bitte.
5. Ich möchte eine Zahnbürste, bitte.
6. Ich möchte ein Brötchen, bitte.

Cartoon confusion

Here you can see how you should have marked the pictures:

Word chain

1. die Zahnbürste
2. der Supermarkt
3. das Brötchen
4. die Postkarte
5. das T-shirt
6. die Torte
7. die Birne
8. der Bleistift
9. die Mütze
10. das Bonbon
11. die Kassette

p.6-7

Market mix-up

The letters that should go in the speech bubbles are:

1. A
2. C
3. B
4. C
5. B
6. A
7. B

Big spenders

A. Sie hat eine Mütze.
B. Du hast ein Eis.
C. Ich habe acht Blumen.
D. Wir haben achtzehn Bonbons.
E. Ihr habt sieben Äpfel.

Clued-up

You should have circled sum D.

p.8-9

Torn in two

1. Ein Kilo Äpfel, bitte.
2. Das macht sechs Mark.
3. Etwas mehr, bitte.
4. Ja, bitte. Und ein Stück Käse.
5. Wo sind die Einkaufskörbe, bitte?
6. Wo sind die Kekse, bitte?

Twin shoppers

Sie hat ein T-Shirt.
Sie hat Käse OR Sie hat ein Stück Käse.
Sie hat einen Bleistift.
Er hat einen Schal.

Er hat Kekse OR Er hat ein Päckchen Kekse.
Er hat einen Comic.

Shopping search

Ich möchte ein T-shirt.
Ich möchte ein Buch.
Ich möchte eine Postkarte.
Ich möchte eine Kassette.
Ich möchte einen Pfirsich.
Ich möchte eine Apfelsine.
Ich möchte ein Poster.
Ich möchte einen Comic.
Ich möchte einen Apfel.

* You can leave **bitte** (please) out of your answers, but to be polite, it is best to add it.

p.10-11

Bargain hunter

The department store Nils should go to is: Billig.
He will spend: dreiunddreißig Mark zwanzig.
He will save: drei Mark fünfzig.

Treasure trail

A. Neben der Bibliothek.
B. Vor dem Käsehändler OR Vor dem Markt.
C. Vor der Bäckerei.
D. Gegenüber von dem Reisebüro.
E. Vor der Drogerie.

The eighth thing on the list is: ein Schal

The shops on Bachstraße

A. die Metzgerei
B. das Fotogeschäft
C. die Post
D. der Plattenladen
E. das Verkehrsamt
F. das Sportgeschäft

p.12-13

Going dotty

Here you can see the maze and, in grey, the route Ute must take through it to find her dog:

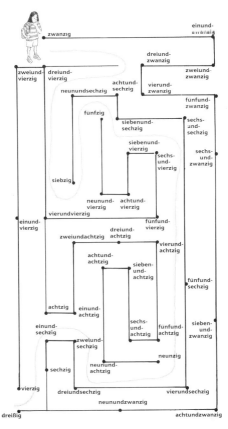

Picture matchmaking

Postcard palaver

1. Entschuldigen Sie. Wo ist **die Post** (**, bitte**)?
2. Ich möchte **eine Briefmarke**, bitte.
3. Für eine **Postkarte**?
4. **Ja**, bitte.
5. **Achtzig Pfennig**, bitte.
6. Ich habe nur **fünfzig Pfennig**.
7. Gibt es hier in der Nähe **eine Bank**?
8. Ja. Auf **der rechten Seite**, neben **der Buchhandlung**.
9. Danke schön. **Auf Wiedersehen**.
10. Wo ist **der Devisenschalter**?
11. Ich möchte **meine Reiseschecks einlösen**, bitte.
12. **Geschlossen**.

p.14-15

Clocking on

1. Der Plattenladen ist von Viertel nach acht morgens bis Viertel vor sieben abends geöffnet.
2. Die Post ist von acht Uhr morgens bis sechs Uhr abends geöffnet.
3. Die Schreibwarenhandlung ist von neun Uhr morgens bis halb sieben abends geöffnet.
4. Die Bibliothek ist von zehn Uhr morgens bis fünf Uhr abends geöffnet.

Word circle

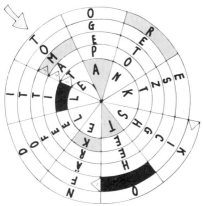

The name you can spell is:
der Markt

Out of time

A. Es ist fünfundzwanzig nach vier.
B. Es ist Viertel nach vier.
C. Es ist vier Uhr.
D. Es ist halb vier.
E. Es ist zehn nach vier.

p.16-17

Which way?

1. die Würstchen
2. die Tomaten
3. die Schokolade
4. das Picknick
5. die Berliner
6. der Orangensaft
7. die Chips
8. die Zwiebeln

Triple treat

1. Sie essen gern Bananen und Eis.
2. Sie ißt gern Apfelsinen und Kekse.
3. Er ißt gern Apfelsinen und Schinken.
4. Er ißt gern Bananen und Äpfel.
5. Sie essen gern Erdbeeren und Bonbons.

Food sails

Getränke:

der Tee
der Orangensaft
das Wasser
der Kaffee

Fleisch:

das Würstchen
der Schinken
die Pastete

Gemüse:

die Kartoffel
die Erbsen
die Karotte
die Zwiebel

Obst:

der Apfel
der Pfirsich
die Aprikose
die Birne
die Apfelsine
die Banane

p.18-19

Sentence splitters

1. Wir essen gern Spaghetti, aber wir essen nicht gern Pommes frites.
2. Ich trinke gern Milch, aber ich trinke nicht gern Orangensaft.
3. Du ißt gern Pizza, aber du ißt nicht gern Suppe.
4. Er trinkt gern Kaffee, aber er trinkt lieber Tee.

German crossword

Crossword grid (answers):
- DIENUDELN
- DERFISCH
- DRACULA
- DASOBST
- DIECHIPS
- DASFLEISCH
- DASBROT
- DASSING...
- DERTEE
- DIELIMO
- DERKUCHEN
- ERTRINKTGERN

The perfect picnic

A. Kirstin
   Stefanie
B. Nils
   Lothar
C. Ute
   Karl

1. Kirstin und Lothar essen gern Kekse.
2. Karl und Ute essen gern Bananen.
3. Karl und Stefanie trinken nicht gern Kaffee.
4. Kirstin und Stefanie essen nicht gern Tomaten.

p.20-21

Hungry campers

A. Greift zu!
B. Reich mir bitte die Konfitüre.
C. Kann ich dir helfen?
D. Schmeckt's?
E. Es schmeckt sehr gut.
F. Noch Brot?
G. Nein, danke. Ich bin satt.

Kitchen caper

Die Butter ist in dem Backofen.
Die Löffel sind in dem Kühlschrank.
Die Teller sind unter dem Tisch.
Der Orangensaft ist auf dem Stuhl.
Die Torte ist in der Spüle.
Die Gabeln sind in der Bratpfanne.
Die Gläser sind auf dem Tisch.
Das Salz ist auf dem Kühlschrank.

Word snake

1. Käse
2. Salz
3. Butter
4. Eier
5. Milch
6. eine Bratpfanne

The word that fits the red grid is:

ein Omelett

p.22-23

Crime cracker

Es ist halb fünf. Ich bin in der Telefonzelle gegenüber von dem Café. Es gibt fünfzehn Menschen in dem Café. Lieselotte Mess ist gegenüber von Uli Gann. Sie ißt einen Salat und er ißt eine Pizza. Ein Brief und zwei Gabeln sind auch auf dem Tisch. Der Kellner bringt einen Orangensaft und einen Tee mit Zitrone.

Taking orders

1. Ich nehme ein Omelett und eine heiße Schokolade.
2. Ich nehme ein Stück Quiche und ein Glas Orangensaft OR Ich nehme eine Quiche und einen Orangensaft.
3. Ich nehme einen Hamburger und ein Glas Cola OR Ich nehme einen Hamburger und eine Cola.
4. Ich nehme einen Salat und ein Glas Orangensaft OR Ich nehme einen Salat und einen Orangensaft.
5. Ich nehme eine Pizza und ein Glas Cola OR Ich nehme eine Pizza und eine Cola.
6. Ich nehme einen Pfannkuchen und einen Kaffee.

Lunch at the Café Paradies

The numbers in the right order are:

5, 8, 3, 6, 4, 1, 7, 2.

p.24-25

Out of order

Here you can see how you should have numbered the orders:

Supper splash-out

A. Eine Pizza mit Salat und einen Hamburger mit Pommes frites, bitte.
B. Reich mir bitte das Wasser.
C. Einen Obstsalat, bitte. Und ein Eis.
D. Ein Vanilleeis, bitte.
E. Die Rechnung, bitte.
F. Ich habe kein Geld!

Word search

1. das Frühstück
2. die Vorspeise
3. der Nachtisch
4. das Restaurant
5. das Glas
6. die Rechnung
7. der Kellner
8. das Steak
9. der Lauch
10. die Cola
11. die Sahne
12. der Kaffee
13. der Löffel
14. das Salz

p.26-27

German crossword

Crossword grid (answers):
- DIEKLEIDER DIE
- DASABENDESSEN
- DERERZ
- DASKAUFHAUS
- DASMEHL DASEIS
- MITTAG
- DIEBUTTER

Cracking codes

Der Supermarkt ist gegenüber von dem Waschsalon. Es gibt eine Frau in dem Supermarkt. Sie hat einen Einkaufswagen. Sie ist in der Nähe von dem Obst. Es gibt Fisch, Apfelsaft und Karotten in dem Einkaufswagen. Die Frau hat eine Tüte. Der Ring ist in der Tüte.

Here you can see where the stolen ring has been hidden:

Poison maze

This is the safe food Stefan will eat:

die Torte
der Apfel
das Eis
die Banane
die Schokolade
die Erdbeere

German-English word list

Here you can find the German words used in this book with their English meanings.

In the plural (when you are talking about more than one thing), many German nouns change (see page 6). Those that add letters are listed here with these letters shown in brackets. For the ones that add an umlaut (¨), or an umlaut and letters, the plural words are shown in full in brackets. Those that do not add anything have (-) after them. Some nouns are only listed in the plural, and these have [pl] after them.

Remember that **der**, **die** and **das** all mean "the", and that in the plural, "the" is **die**.

das Abendessen	dinner (evening meal)
abends	in the evening
aber	but
acht	eight
also	well, so
am	by the, at the
am Ende der Straße	at the end of the street
der Apfel (die Äpfel)	apple
der Apfelsaft	apple juice
die Apfelsine(-n)	orange
der Apfelstrudel	apple strudel
die Apotheke(-n)	chemist's, pharmacy
die Aprikose(-n)	apricot
auch	also, as well
auf	on
auf der linken Seite	on the left
auf der rechten Seite	on the right
der Aufkleber(-)	sticker
auf Wiedersehen	goodbye
der Ausgang (die Ausgänge)	exit
die Bäckerei(-en)	baker's
der Backofen (die Backöfen)	oven
der Ball (die Bälle)	ball
die Banane(-n)	banana
die Bank(-en)	bank
der Baum (die Bäume)	tree
der Becher(-)	plastic cup, beaker
das Bekleidungs-geschäft(-e)	clothes shop
das Benzin	petrol
der Berliner(-)	doughnut
die Bibliothek(-en)	library
die Birne(-n)	pear
bitte	please
bitte schön	there you go, there you are
bitte sehr?	what would you like?
der Bleistift(-e)	pencil
die Blume(-n)	flower

der Blumenkohl	cauliflower
das Bonbon(-s)	sweet
die Bratpfanne(-n)	frying pan
der Brief(-e)	letter
die Briefmarke(-n)	stamp
bringen	to bring
das Brot	bread
das Brötchen(-)	bread roll
die Brote [pl]	sandwiches
das Buch (die Bücher)	book
die Buchhandlung (-en)	bookshop
die Butter	butter
das Café(-s)	café
die Champignons [pl]	mushrooms
die Chips [pl]	crisps
die Cola(-s)	coke
der Comic(-s)	comic
da drüben	over there
danke (schön)	thank you (very much)
das Essen ist fertig	come to the table, it's ready
das macht	that comes to
das Öl kontrollieren	to check the oil
das Stück	each
der Detektiv(-e)	detective
Deutschland	Germany
der Devisenschalter(-)	foreign exchange desk
drei	three
die Drogerie(-n)	chemist's
du	you
die Eier [pl]	eggs
ein/eine	a, an, one
eine Scheibe	a slice (of)
eine Tüte Chips	a packet of crisps
der Eingang (die Eingänge)	entrance
ein Glas	a glass (of)
der Einkaufskorb (die Einkaufskörbe)	basket
der Einkaufswagen (-)	trolley
ein Kilo	a kilo (of)
ein Päckchen	a packet (of)
eins	one
ein Stück	a piece (of)
das Eis(-)	ice-cream
entschuldigen Sie	excuse me
Entschuldigung	sorry
er	he, it
die Erbsen [pl]	peas
die Erdbeere(-n)	strawberry
das Erdbeereis	strawberry ice-cream
er/sie liest	he/she is reading
es	it
es gibt	there is/are
es ist	it is
es ist kein/keine ... mehr da	there is no more ...
es ist ... Uhr	it is ... o'clock
es schmeckt sehr gut	it's delicious

essen	to eat
es tut mir leid	I'm sorry
das Etui(-s)	pencil case
etwas mehr	a little more
etwas weniger	a little less
das Feinkostgeschäft(-e)	delicatessen
der Film(-e)	film
der Fisch	fish
das Fleisch	meat
das Fotogeschäft(-e)	camera shop
fragen	to ask
Frau	Mrs.
die Frau(-en)	woman
das Frühstück	breakfast
fünf	five
für	for
die Gabel(-n)	fork
gegenüber von	opposite
das Geld	money
das Gemüse	vegetables
der Gemüsehändler(-)	greengrocer's
geöffnet	open
das Geschäft(-e)	shop, store
geschlossen	closed
die Getränke [pl]	drinks
gibt es hier in der Nähe ein/eine ...?	is there a ... near here?
das Glas (die Gläser)	glass
greif zu, greifen Sie zu, greift zu	help yourself/help yourselves
guten Abend	good evening
guten Appetit	enjoy your meal
guten Morgen	good morning
guten Tag	hello, good day
haben	to have, to have got
das Hähnchen(-)	chicken
halb	half
halb (acht/neun ...)	half past (seven/eight ...)
der Hamburger(-)	hamburger
hast du?, habt ihr?, haben Sie?	do you have?
das Hauptgericht (-e)	main course
das Heft(-e)	exercise book
die heiße Schokolade	hot chocolate
Herr	Mr.
hinter	behind
hundert Gramm	a hundred grammes (of)
ich bin	I am
ich bin satt	I've had enough (to eat)
ich bin Vegetarier/ Vegetarierin	I am a vegetarian
ich esse gern	I like (eating)
ich esse lieber	I prefer (eating)
ich esse nicht	I do not eat
ich esse nicht gern	I do not like (eating)
ich habe Durst	I'm thirsty
ich habe Hunger	I'm hungry
ich möchte	I would like

ich möchte meine Reiseschecks einlösen	I would like to cash my traveller's cheques
ich nehme	I'll have
ich trinke gern	I like (drinking)
ich trinke lieber	I prefer (drinking)
ihr	you
in	in
in der Nähe von	near
ist	is
ja	yes
jamjam!	yum yum!
der Kaffee	coffee
kann ich dir/euch/ Ihnen helfen?	can I help you?
die Karotte(-n)	carrot
die Kartoffel(-n)	potato
der Käse	cheese
das Käsebrot(-e)	cheese sandwich
der Käsehändler(-)	cheese seller, cheese stall
die Kassette(-n)	cassette
das Kaufhaus (die Kaufhäuser)	department store
kein/keine	no, none
der Keks(-e)	biscuit
der Kellner(-)	waiter
der Kiosk(-e)	kiosk
die Kleider [pl]	clothes
der Kochtopf (die Kochtöpfe)	saucepan
die Konditorei(-en)	cake shop
die Konfitüre	jam
könnten Sie?	could you?
die Küche(-n)	kitchen
der Kühlschrank (die Kühlschränke)	fridge
der Lauch	leek, leeks
das Lineal(-e)	ruler
der Löffel(-)	spoon
die Mark(-)	mark (money)
der Markt (die Märkte)	market
das Mehl	flour
die Menschen [pl]	people
das Messer(-)	knife
die Metzgerei(-en)	butcher's
die Milch	milk
mit	with
mit Milch	with milk
Mittag	midday, twelve o'clock
das Mittagessen	lunch
mit Zitrone	with lemon
das Mokkaeis	coffee ice-cream
morgens	in the morning
die Mütze(-n)	cap
nach	past (with a time)
der Nachtisch(-e)	dessert, pudding
neben	next to
nein	no
neun	nine
noch ...?	some more...?
noch ein/noch eine	another
die Nudeln [pl]	pasta
nur	only
das Obst	fruit
der Obstsalat(-e)	fruit salad
oder	or

das Omelett(-e)	omelette
der Orangensaft	orange juice
der Paß (die Pässe)	passport
die Pastete	pâté
der Pfannkuchen(-)	pancake
der Pfennig(-e)	pfennig (money)
der Pfirsich(-e)	peach
die Pflaster [pl]	plasters
das Picknick(-s)	picnic
die Pizza(-s)	pizza
der Plattenladen (die Plattenläden)	music shop
die Pommes frites [pl]	chips
die Post	post office
das Poster(-)	poster
die Postkarte(-n)	postcard
die Quiche	quiche
die Rechnung(-en)	bill
reichen Sie mir bitte .../reich mir bitte ...	can you pass me ..., please?
das Reisebüro(-s)	travel agent's
die Reiseschecks [pl]	traveller's cheques
das Restaurant(-s)	restaurant
der Ring(-e)	ring
die Sahne	cream
der Salat(-e)	salad
das Salz	salt
der Schal(´-s)	scarf
der Schinken	ham
das Schinkenbrot (-e)	ham sandwich
schmeckt's?	is it good?
die Schokolade	chocolate
die Schokoladencreme	chocolate mousse
das Schokoladeneis	chocolate ice-cream
die Schreibwaren-handlung(-en)	stationer's
sechs	six
sie	she, it, they
Sie	you (polite)
sieben	seven
sind	are
die Sonnenbrille(-n)	sunglasses
sonst noch etwas?	anything else?
soviel?	this much?, like that?
die Spaghetti [pl]	spaghetti
die Speisekarte(-n)	menu
der Spinat	spinach
die Sportartikel [pl]	sports gear
das Sportgeschäft (-e)	sports shop
die Spüle(-n)	sink
das Steak(-s)	steak
die Straße(-n)	street
das Stück Torte(-)	piece/slice of cake
der Stuhl (die Stühle)	chair
der Supermarkt (die Supermärkte)	supermarket
die Suppe(-n)	soup
das Tagesgericht	dish of the day, "today's special"
das Tagesmenü(-s)	set menu
die Tankstelle(-n)	petrol station

der Tee	tea
die Telefonzelle(-n)	phone booth
der Teller(-)	plate
der Tisch(-e)	table
die Toiletten [pl]	toilets
die Tomate(-n)	tomato
die Torte(-n)	cake
trinken	to drink
das T-shirt(-s)	T-shirt
die Tüte(-n)	bag
um (sechs Uhr)	at (six o'clock)
und	and
und als Nachtisch?	and (what would you like) for dessert?
unter	under
das Vanilleeis	vanilla ice-cream
das Verkehrsamt (die Verkehrsämter)	tourist office
vier	four
Viertel nach/vor	quarter past/to
volltanken?	shall I fill her up (with petrol)?
volltanken, bitte	fill her up, please
von ... bis	from ... until
vor	in front of, to (with a time)
die Vorspeise(-n)	starter
das Waschpulver	washing powder
der Waschsalon(-s)	launderette
was für ein Eis?	what flavour ice-cream?
was kostet das?	how much is it/that?
was macht das?	how much does that come to?
das Wasser	water
wie spät ist es?	what time is it?
wo ist/sind?	where is/are?
das Würstchen(-)	sausage
die Zahnbürste(-n)	toothbrush
zehn	ten
der Zeitungshändler(-)	newsagent's
der Zucker	sugar
zwei	two
die Zwiebel(-n)	onion
zwischen	between

First published in 1993 by Usborne Publishing Ltd, 83-85 Saffron Hill, London EC1N 8RT, England.

Copyright © 1993 Usborne Publishing Ltd.

The name Usborne and the device ⌐ are Trade Marks of Usborne Publishing Ltd. All rights reserved. No part of this publication may be reproduced, stored in a retrieval system, or transmitted in any form or by any means, electronic, mechanical, photocopying, recording or otherwise, without the prior permission of the publisher.

Printed in Portugal.